It's My BEDTIME...
But I'm THIRSTY!
(and other famous stalls)

by Shannon Benish

Illustrated By Judith Bicking

Dedicated to Erin and Evan,
true masters of the bedtime stall.

And to Grandpa Hemken, for the fond memories of sleepover nights
watching Johnny Carson in the living room and wondering what a
"bed bug" was.

Free coloring pages can be downloaded at:
www.eepurl.com/dpdlcL

1

It's my bedtime... but I'm thirsty!
Can I have a drink?

It's my bedtime... but my feet are cold.
I need my bunny slippers!

It's my bedtime... but these aren't my
dinosaur pajamas.
I need my favorite pajamas!

It's my bedtime... but I'm hungry!
Can I have a snack?

It's my bedtime... but I need to
go potty!

10

It's my bedtime... but it's too dark.
I need my nightlight!

It's my bedtime... but I need my friend.
Where's Teddy?!

It's my bedtime... but it's too quiet!
Can I listen to music?

It's my bedtime... but I want to cuddle.
I need my blankie!

It's my bedtime... but it's still too dark.
I need a flashlight!

It's my bedtime... but I miss Grandma.
Can we call Grandma?

It's my bedtime... but I think there's a
monster under my bed.
Can we check?

24

It's my bedtime... but my feet are still cold.
I need socks!

It's my bedtime... but I need to go potty again!

It's my bedtime... but I forgot to brush my teeth!

It's my bedtime... but I need a story!
Can you tell me a story?

It's my bedtime... but I need a hug.
Can I please have a hug?

It's my bedtime... but I love you.
Do you love me too?

"Yes honey, I love you to the moon and back."

"Sweet dreams, sleep tight. Don't let the bed bugs bite!"

ZZZZZ...   THE END...
(Until tomorrow.)

42

ABOUT THE AUTHOR

Shannon Benish
is a financial advisor
and lives in Dodge City,
Kansas with her husband
John, children
Erin, Evan and step-
daughter Sydney.

She enjoys attending her
children's activities, doing
home repair, reading,
movies, travel, and
watching football.
She has also authored
the book How To Help
Someone With Cancer

Follow her on Twitter
@ShannonBenish

Made in the USA
Monee, IL
23 November 2022

18306545R10031